TEST
YOUR
ENGLISH

ISBN 0 7169 5515 6
© *Robert Gibson & Sons, 1997*

ROBERT GIBSON • Publisher
17 Fitzroy Place, Glasgow, G3 7SF.

FOREWORD

The 40 exercises in this book were designed for older primary and younger secondary school pupils, but are suitable also for students learning English as a second language.

They are suitable both for class use and for those working on their own for examinations.

The aspects of language covered by the questions range from vocabulary and meaning, through basic grammar and punctuation, to sentence construction and composition in all its variety.

In addition, many questions are designed to promote confidence and fluency in the use of words by ensuring familiarity with those idiomatic expressions (similes, metaphors and proverbs, for example) which are so typical of the English language.

Where the user of the book has difficulty with questions of a particular kind, reference to the Analysis of Exercises on the opposite page will show where practice with similar questions is provided. The column headed 'NFA' shows the pages where further examples, often with explanations, may be found in New First Aid in English (also published by Robert Gibson & Sons).

ANALYSIS OF EXERCISES

3

EXERCISE 1

1. Divide into the subject (naming part) and predicate (telling part) the following sentences:
   (a) The sun shone brightly.
   (b) I called for my brother.

2. Make a list of the nouns in the following:
   (a) The hen and her chickens were in the garden.
   (b) The man and woman met in the train.
   (c) The vase of flowers stood on the table.

3. Punctuate the following, putting in capital letters where necessary:
   (a) mary said that her sister ruth had gone to london
   (b) the man was selling apples cherries pears and plums

4. Give the plural of:
   box ....   loaf ....
   banjo ....   dwarf ....
   hero ....   deer ....
   woman ....   ox ....

5. Write the feminine gender of:—
   actor ....   duke ....
   friar ....   brother ....
   bachelor ....   colt ....
   hero ....   sir ....

6. We speak of a *flock* of sheep. Write in the spaces, the correct word for:
   a .... of fish   a .... of cattle
   a .... of trees   a .... of drawers
   a .... of ships   a .... of furniture
   a .... of flowers   a .... of chickens

7. Complete the following:
   as blind as ....   as busy as ....
   as bold as ....   as cold as ....
   as dead as ....   as fat as ....
   as pleased as ....   as quiet as ....

8. Write a short description of about five lines of:—
   (a) A postage stamp;
   and
   (b) A football.

EXERCISE 2

1. Divide into subject and predicate:
   (a) Flakes of snow fell to-day.
   (b) Yesterday, I saw my uncle.

2. Give the singular of:

   gases ....   men ....

   mice ....   ladies ....

   wolves ....   potatoes ....

   thieves ....   feet ....

3. Make a list of the verbs in the following paragraph:
   "I sheltered under the tree while the rain fell heavily, and I knew that my hopes of a picnic had vanished. I decided to return home and pass the afternoon reading my favourite books."

4. Punctuate, inserting capital letters where necessary:
   (a) when i met jim he asked me if i would come to cardiff on the four oclock train.
   (b) did you meet your father asked john

5. Write sentences to show the difference between:
   Boar, bore;   check, cheque;   bean, been;   core, corps.

6. Give a word opposite in meaning to:

   absent ....   bitter ....

   love ....   reveal ....

   war ....   open ....

   never ....   good ....

7. Complete these proverbs and explain the meaning of two of them:
   A bird in hand ....
   A fool and his money ....
   All's well ....

8. Imagine you are a bird living in a cage. Describe in about 15 lines:
   "A day in my life."

EXERCISE 3

1. Divide into subject and predicate:
   (a) Under the tree, a man was standing.
   (b) Every cloud has a silver lining.

2. Make a list of adjectives in this paragraph:
   He was a selfish old man, who lived alone in a shabby house near the main road. He was dressed in a brown suit and on his feet were leather sandals. His dark skin and black beard made little children afraid of him, but the older folk knew that he would do them no injury.

3. Write out the following sentences, using the correct word from the brackets:
   The girls sat .... reading .... books.   (their, there)
   This ....cap.   (his, is)
   It is .... far .... walk.   (to, too)

4. Correct the following sentences:
   He was the youngest of the two boys.
   Tom has broke his arm.
   Between you and I, it is not true.
   We seen many people on the beach.

5. Form a noun from:

please	....	strong	....
give	....	grow	....
act	....	proud	....
gay	....		

6. Complete:

as slow as	....	as smooth as	....
as tough as	....	as white as	....
as thick as	....	as hungry as	....
as fierce as	....	as brown as	....

7. Give the feminine gender of:—

count	....	beau	....
lad	....	monk	....
uncle	....	wizard	....
waiter	....	prophet	....

8. Write a letter to your mother, who has been away for a week, telling her all that has happened since she left.

EXERCISE 4

1. Divide into subject and predicate:
   (a) The birds flew from tree to tree.
   (b) By the fire, the cat was sleeping.

2. Give the plural of:

army	....	tooth	....
child	....	goose	....
hoof	....	piano	....
slave	....	salmon	....
knife	....	man	....

3. Give the masculine gender of:

heiress	....	wife	....
mistress	....	mama	....
she	....	sister	....
mare	....	heifer	....

4. Write sentences containing the phrases:
   Again and again;   ways and means;   part and parcel;
   rough and ready;   give and take.

5. Write a word similar in meaning to:—

astonish	....	empty	....
join	....	small	....
mariner	....	moisture	....
permit	....	cease	....

6. Form adjectives from:

beauty	....	length	....
poet	....	pity	....
hope	....	peril	....
noise	....	mourn	....

7. Use the correct word from those in the brackets:
   He (begun, began) the service as soon as the bell (rang, rung).
   No sooner had I (spoke, spoken) than a rabbit (sprang, sprung) out of the hedge.
   I was (took, taken) to identify the parcel he had (given, gave) me.
   He has (grew, grown) up near the place where the man was (slew, slain).

8. Write a short description of:
   (a) Your favourite wild bird.
   (b) Your favourite wild flower.

EXERCISE 5

1. Add suitable predicates to these subjects:—
   The squirrel ....
   Some people ....
   In summer, the sun ....

2. Give the plural of these pronouns:

I	....	she	....
it	....	you	....
mine	....	him	....
he	....		

3. Use another word instead of *nice* to describe the following:

a .... hat	a .... niece
a .... tea	a .... concert
a .... book	a .... flower
a .... orange	a .... surprise

4. Explain the meaning of:
   To go through the mill;   To come a cropper;
   To strike while the iron's hot;   To get into hot water.

5. Give the past tense of:—

am	....	begin	....	lie	....
tear	....	speak	....	fight	....
do	....	catch	....		

6. Complete the following comparisons:—

Positive	Comparative	Superlative
fast	faster	fastest
late	....	....
beautiful	....	....
good	....	....
tall	....	....
many	....	....

7. Write in full:

can't	....	I'll	....	all's ....
it's	....	hasn't	....	o'er ....
he's	....	shouldn't	....	

8. Write a letter to a friend wishing him/her:
   "Many happy returns of the day."

1. Supply a suitable subject to each predicate:—
   (a) .... blew hard all day.
   (b) .... passed overhead.
   (c) .... were damaged by the bombs.
   (d) .... scored a wonderful goal.

2. Make a list of five of each of the following kinds of nouns:
   proper ....   common ....
   collective ....   abstract ....

3. Form a verb from:
   civil ....   knee ....
   relief ....   pure ....
   fertile ....   sharp ....
   frost ....   courage ....

4. Use the correct word from each bracket:
   He was (hair, heir) to the (throne, thrown).
   I bought a (pear, pair) of (soles, souls) for my shoes.
   I (ate, eight) a (serial, cereal) for breakfast.
   He hit the (bale, bail) off with the first (ball, bawl).
   I have lost the (quay, key) to the (main, mane) door.

5. Explain the meaning of:
   Once bitten, twice shy.
   Robbing Peter to pay Paul.
   When the cat's away, the mice will play.

6. Give one word for:
   The front part of a ship   ....
   A fertile spot in a desert   ....
   A boy who frightens smaller boys   ....
   A place for storing motor cars   ....
   The flesh of a pig   ....

7. Complete the following:—

Positive	Comparative	Superlative
....	colder	....
famous	....	....
....	....	worst
funny	....	....
....	better	....

8. Write a story entitled: "The most exciting day in my life."

9

EXERCISE 7

1. Draw a rectangle 152 mm long by 90 mm wide to represent an envelope. Address it to yourself at your home address. Draw an outline of the stamp in position.

2. By means of a prefix give the opposite of the following words:
   like .... possible ....
   use .... legal ....
   regular ....

3. Write these sentences in the plural:
   The cargo was carried to the ship.
   The mouse ran into its hole.
   He played the banjo at the dance.
   The man-of-war struck the reef.

4. Use the correct form of the verb at the beginning of each sentence:
   begin   The meeting had only just ....
   see   I have often .... him there.
   sing   She .... at the concert.
   blow   The dust has .... into the room.
   fly   The bird .... over the hedge.

5. Complete the proverbs:
   A bad workman   ....
   Fine feathers   ....
   Fair exchange is ....
   Every cloud   ....

6. What is meant by:
   A storm in a teacup;   The lion's share;
   A bird's eye view;   A white elephant?

7. Give one word for:
   Goods sent out of the country   ....
   A place where people are buried ....
   A place where iron goods are made ....
   The top of a hill or mountain   ....

8. Write a letter to a friend inviting him to join you on a picnic.

EXERCISE 8

1. Change all masculines to feminines:
   The husband was a Jew.
   His father is a widower.
   The son and his uncle were present.
   Lord Manfield gave his nephew a new car.

2. Complete:

as cunning as	....	as clear as	....
as strong as	....	as right as	....
as white as	....	as proud as	....
as happy as	....	as fit as	....

3. Fill in the blanks to complete the following:

the .... roars		the .... hisses	
the .... howls		the .... bellows	
the .... squeaks		the .... neighs	

4. Give a word opposite in meaning to:

accept	....	east	....
superior	....	selfish	....
rude	....	praise	....
first	....	opaque	....

5. Write sentences using the following words to show the difference in meaning:
   Pores, pours; tail, tale; sale, sail; none, nun; dessert, desert; ceiling, sealing.

6. Explain the meaning of:
   Down in the mouth; Out of sorts; Stuck up; To smell a rat; To act the goat.

7. Form an adjective from:

circle	....	obey	....
star	....	silver	....
rag	....	marvel	....
France	....	crime	....

8. Write a short description of:
   (a) A pair of scissors.
   (b) A school desk.

EXERCISE 9

1. Punctuate the following, putting in all capitals and quotation marks where necessary:

    stop shouted tom i want you to post a letter for me all right i replied ill call for it on my way

2. Give one word for:

    An institution where lunatics are kept ....
    A field in which fruit trees grow ....
    A place where beer is made ....
    A person who saves and hoards his money ....
    A three-sided figure ....

3. Select the correct word from the brackets, and write each sentence:

    (Who, Whom) do you think I saw at the (shew, show)?
    Last (knight, night) I played in (gaol, goal).
    (Were, Was) you at the (plaice, place) I mentioned?
    He threw the (peel, peal) into the (great, grate).

4. Give the noun formed from:

    beautiful   ....   anxious   ....
    satisfy   ....   wise   ....
    oppose   ....   false   ....
    creditable   ....   attract   ....

5. Compare these adjectives:

Positive	Comparative	Superlative
long	....	....
thin	....	....
little	....	....
generous	....	....
gay	....	....

6. Give the meaning of:

    B.C.; C.O.D.; l.b.w.; U.S.A.; P.O.; O.H.M.S.; p.m.; Mrs.

7. Put in the apostrophe:

    The girls dress was torn.
    The boys pencils were collected.
    The childrens books were marked by the teacher.
    I found a womans glove in the shop.
    The window was full of ladies bags.

8. Write a description of any two of these:
   (a) A walk down a country lane.
   (b) A visit to a museum.
   (c) A day's fishing.

EXERCISE 10

1. Choose the correct word from the brackets and write out the sentence:
   The girl has (ate, eaten) a pear and (drunk, drank) some lemonade.
   The letter (come, came) by post to-day.
   We (saw, seen) the prisoner running away.
   He asked me if I had (broken, broke) the cup.
   Tom has (took, taken) the parcel to the station.

2. Change all masculines to feminine:
   The manservant spoke to the earl.
   The bridegroom rode in the master's car.
   I sold the colt to him.
   The cock-sparrow was caught by the tom-cat.

3. Arrange the following words in the order in which they would appear in a dictionary:
   (a) Brown, but, been, branch, baby, beautiful.
   (b) Piper, plain, pity, plane, puzzle, plan.
   (c) Soft, sale, stale, sugar, shape, spite.

4. Use an apostrophe to write these sentences in a shorter way:
   I will go to the match.
   I told him to come at ten *of the* clock.
   I *could not* go to the party.
   I would like to be present.
   It is raining.

5. Fill in the blanks, with the correct word from the brackets:—
   I will .... you to sing.   (learn, teach).
   She is going to .... down.   (lie, lay).
   The murderer was .... to-day.   (hung, hanged).
   I .... be pleased to accept.   (shall, will).
   The tenant's rent was ....   (risen, raised).

13

6. Complete the following:
    Girl is to boy as .... is to man.
    Shoe is to foot as .... is to hand.
    Nephew is to uncle as .... is to aunt.
    Tall is to short as .... is to white.
    Green is to grass as .... is to berry.

7. Give one word for:
    A religious song ....
    Another name for a donkey ....
    A man who does tricks with cards, etc. ....
    A man who pretends to be good ....
    A small river ....

8. Write a letter to your teacher explaining why you have been kept home from school.

EXERCISE 11

1. Substitute one word for those in italics:
    The *people who were listening* were pleased.
    Owing to the fog, the ship was *unable to be seen*.
    He had made his plans *with care*.
    You should practise being *in time*.
    He is a young man who is *anxious to succeed*.

2. Fill in the spaces with suitable collective nouns:
    I met a .... of wolves in the forest.
    The .... of magistrates listened to the case.
    A .... of musicians played in the street.
    The robbery was carried out by a .... of thieves.
    I bought a .... of golf clubs for my father.

3. Give a word opposite in meaning to:

early	....	bless	....
often	....	noise	....
sober	....	tame	....
timid	....	victory	....

4. Use the correct pronoun from each of the brackets:
    Tom is much heavier than (he, him).
    She is almost as strong as (me, I).
    The dog growled at my brother and (I, me).
    John and (her, she) jumped into the water.
    (We, us) girls were playing hockey.

14

5. Rewrite these sentences without using the word *got* so that the meaning is not altered:
    I got up early to-day.
    She got a bad cold.
    They got their luggage from the station.
    I got a penny in my pocket.
    I got to the dance at nine o'clock.

6. Complete the proverbs, and explain the meaning of two of them:
    A friend in need ....
    A miss is as good ....
    A rolling stone ....
    A stitch in time ....

7. Form compound nouns from the following words by joining pairs of words:
    Ache, ball, paper, tray, tooth, maid, fly, ash, stone, post, milk, foot, man, tomb, door, servant.

8. Imagine you are a postman. Describe a typical day in your life.

EXERCISE 12

1. Correct the following sentences:
    Peter was the biggest of the two boys.
    The match was won by the best team.
    "Don't walk so quick" said Joan.
    Mary ate the larger of the three pears.
    To who did you give the letter?

2. Insert the capitals, and punctuate the following:
    i took my sisters dress to mr jones who has a cleaning business
    i didnt know until sunday that aunt jane was going to france

3. Insert the name of the sound in these sentences:
    I heard the .... of the frog.
    The .... of the bear could be heard at the Zoo.
    A cat .... when feeling happy.
    I heard the .... of silk as she passed by.

4. Choose the word in each line that is different from the others:
    Beech, oak, turnip, elm, ash   ....
    John, Jim, Jack, Jane, Jacob   ....
    Saucer, plate, dish, cup, spoon   ....
    Germany, Paris, Sweden, Spain, Holland   ....
    Eagle, lion, tiger, puma, elephant   ....

15

5. Use in sentences:

Fits and starts; Free and easy; Hue and cry;
Round and round; Wear and tear.

6. Complete:

Cat is to mouse as spider is to ....
Dog is to puppy as .... is to kitten.
April is to May as .... is to August.
Ancient is to .... as rich is to poor.
Shoal is to fish as .... is to bees.

7. Give a word similar in meaning to:

circular	....	cunning	....
enemy	....	elude	....
valour	....	surrender	....
myth	....	persuade	....

8. Write a description of the night that you were:
"Caught in a thunderstorm."

EXERCISE 13

1. Form a verb from:

friend	....	life	....
moisture	....	clear	....
circle	....	beauty	....
roll	....	tomb	....

2. Give the present tense of:

ate	....	lost	....
bitten	....	flew	....
awoke	....	rose	....
swept	....	froze	....

3. Give the comparative and superlative of:

small	....	bad	....
much	....	cautious	....
elegant	....	lovely	....

4. Complete the sentences by using a suitable word in the space:

I opened the window to have a .... of fresh air.
A .... of paper fell to the floor.
There was a .... of dust in his eye.
She cut a .... of hair from his head.
I felt a .... of rain on my face.

16

5. Explain the meaning of:
    Thick in the head;   At rest;   A queer fish;
    To sweep the board;   To take French leave.

6. Substitute one word for:
    A hundred years   ....
    A woman in charge of a hospital   ....
    The men who work on board a ship at sea   ....
    The first meal of the day   ....
    A place where leather is made   ....

7. Write these sentences in the plural.
    She placed the scissors on the table.
    The child saw the ox in the field.
    The baby held the lady's hand.
    The wife attended the cookery class.
    The palm tree grew in the oasis.

8. Write a letter in reply to one of the following advertisements:
    (a) New bicycles for immediate delivery. Catalogue of models and prices free on request.

    A.S.M. Cycles Ltd., Coventry.

    (b) Rug making for profit. Samples, canvas and wool with full details, for 30p stamp.

    Alpha Mills, Bradford, 2.

EXERCISE 14

1. The following words have more than one meaning. Write sentences to show this difference:
    Pen, row, minute, round, bank.

2. Rewrite the following sentences, using one word for those in italics:
    When the telegram arrived, I returned home *at once*.
    The *people who live next door* own a parrot.
    I tried to find him, but he had *passed out of sight*.
    He was *not pleased* when he heard the news.
    I met my *father's brother* at the station.

17

3. Add one word to complete these "doubles":

shoulder to	....	such and	....
by and	....	null and	....
safe and	....	here and	....

4. Name the places where you would expect the following to live:

a vicar	....	a monk	....
a snail	....	a pig	....
a rector	....	a convict	....
a tiger	....		

5. Complete the following by the use of a suitable word:

I passed a .... of motor-cars going to the fair.

I ran down the .... of steps.

From the ship we saw a .... of whales.

Mary bought a .... of wool to finish her jumper.

The farmer carried a .... of hay to the cattle.

6. Give the name of the following:

A room in a house, situated just under the roof.

A residence with all rooms on the ground floor.

A man who draws and paints.

A stream which flows into the main river.

A place where whisky is made.

7. Use in sentences, to show the difference in meaning:

Loan, lone;	scene, seen;	prophet, profit;
leak, leek;	currant, current.	

8. Write a letter to your cousin inviting him/her to spend the weekend at your home.

EXERCISE 15

1. Give one word for:

Low ground between two hills	....
A vessel for holding flowers	....
A room on board a ship	....
A tin for holding tea	....
A funny drawing in a newspaper	....

2. Correct the following sentences:
   He drunk it very quickly.
   My mother told me to lay down.
   I met the man what found the jewels.
   The tree had fell across the road.
   After the game, the boy shouted, "We won you."

3. Give a word opposite in meaning to:

hollow	....	heroic	....
barren	....	temporary	....
transparent	....	freedom	....
public	....	unite	....

4. Write in full:

P.T.O.	....	St.	....	Pl.	....
P.S.	....	Ave.	....	T.U.C.	....
J.P.	....	G.P.O	....	B.B.C.	....
M.P.	....				

5. Form a noun from:

absent	....	thrive	....
warm	....	equal	....
famous	....	strong	....
divide	....	conclude	....

6. In the blanks, write one of the prepositions:
   From, among, to, between, in.
   The player appealed .... the referee.
   Your ruler is different .... mine.
   The sweets were shared .... the four girls.
   I sat .... the two boys.
   Fashions are different .... Russia.

7. Explain the meaning of:
   To hit below the belt;   To pull his leg;
   To send to Coventry;   To face the music.

8. Describe the kind of work you would like to do when you leave school.

1. Complete the sentences by using the words in the brackets:

I think .... mother .... ill.   (is, his)

I don't know whether .... father was ....   (there, their)

He .... much money as you.   (as, has)

I would like to know .... you .... last night.   (where, were)

2. Put in the apostrophe:

The pupils books were collected.

The childrens shoes were cleaned.

He decorated the horses manes with ribbon.

The babys bonnet was lost.

3. Write in the plural:

The girl gave her ribbon to her friend.

This is a beautiful drawing.

The salmon was swimming in the river.

I like to watch a good play.

4. Rewrite the following sentences, using a word opposite in meaning to the word in italics:

He has now secured a *permanent* post.

His house was on an *exposed* site.

The prisoner was *released*.

I *frequently* meet him in the street.

His work is *superior* to mine.

5. Form compound words from the following:

spend, mill, craft, thrift, post, tea, stone, witch, lamp, cup.

6. Form a verb from the following words:

knee	....	rich	....
knowledge	....	wide	....
food	....	fat	....
dark	....	critic	....
full	....	blood	....

7. Where would you look in order to find:

A record of attendance at school?   ....

A telephone number?   ....

The meaning of a word?   ....

The position of a place?   ....

The address of a person?   ....

8. Describe what you would do in any two of the following:
   (a) If you lost your way in a big city.
   (b) If your friend's dress caught fire.
   (c) If you saw smoke coming from a closed store.

EXERCISE 17

1. Use in sentences:
   Before very long;   Little by little;
   Without delay;   As far as I know.

2. Give one word for:
   A place where sky and sea seem to meet.
   A person who writes songs.
   A shop selling milk and butter.
   A woman whose husband is dead.
   A man who prepares plans of buildings.

3. Put in the capital letters and punctuation where necessary:
   (a) edinburgh is the capital of scotland
   (b) peter and may who were married yesterday went to spain for their honeymoon

4. Make a list of the pronouns in this passage:
   She told me that her mother would return the book as soon as she had finished
   reading it.

5. Make sentences using the following words, so that the difference in meaning is
   shown:
   Aisle, isle; blue, blew; mail, male; peer, pier; wait, weight.

6. Complete these:
   Better late   ....   Every dog   ....
   Birds of a feather   ....   Faint heart ....

7. Give a word similar in meaning to:
   affectionate   ....   raiment   ....
   residence   ....   obstinate ....
   minimum   ....   terror   ....
   tranquil   ....   immense   ....

8. Describe briefly:
   (a) How you would mend a puncture;
   or
   (b) How you would darn a sock.

21

EXERCISE 18

1. Punctuate:
    The teacher said close the door
    You need not call to-night replied Susie
    Tim asked the porter what time is the next train
    When I have finished my sums said Carol I will be able to join you

2. Rewrite in the plural:
    The army carried out a new exercise.
    The bird was perched on the roof.
    His son-in-law plays football.
    The cargo was loaded on a barge.
    The fisherman caught a trout.

3. Change all the feminines to masculines:
    My niece is a spinster.
    "Yes, madam," she replied.
    She is the heiress to her mother's estate.
    The filly was attacked by the tigress.
    The sisters thanked the hostess before leaving.

4. Insert a suitable collective noun to complete the sentence:
    A .... of people attended the football match.
    There was a large .... present at the evening service.
    The celebrity concert attracted a large ....
    A .... of hooligans took part in the riot.

5. Name the occupation of the person who would use:—

a joy-stick	....	a razor	....
a spanner	....	an anvil	....
a wig	....	handcuffs	....
a pulpit	....	a typewriter	....

6. Use in sentences:
    Neck and neck;   Over and over;   Odds and ends;
    Spick and span;   On and off.

7. Select the correct word from the brackets and write out the sentence:
    The (beach, beech) trees were fully (grown, groan).
    The (grate, great) had a faulty (flew, flue).
    He (mist, missed) meeting the (mayor, mare) at the ball.
    There was a (hoard, horde) of savages in the (picture, pitcher).
    I did (not, knot) join the (choir, quire).

8. Write a telegram to your father informing him that you will arrive home on the nine o'clock train, asking him to meet you at the station.

EXERCISE 19

1. Form adjectives from:

continent	....	mystery	....
wool	....	worth	....
voice	....	vanity	....
nation	....	melody	....

2. Correct these sentences:
   His hair needs cutting badly.
   It was her you saw.
   She is worse than me.
   We seen him there last night.

3. Select one word from each of the brackets and then write each sentence:
   My mother helped me to (ring, wring) the clothes.
   I will (write, right) to the R.A.C. for a (root, route) to Brighton.
   The child was not (aloud, allowed) to (by, buy) the toy.
   I (tolled, told) (him, hymn) not to (waist, waste) (time, thyme).
   My sister (one, won) a (pair, pare) of vases.

4. Give one word for:
   A man who protects sheep.   ....
   A girl who serves at table.   ....
   A metal container to hold coal.   ....
   A name for smuggled goods.   ....
   "Way out" sign above a door.   ....

5. Add the proper collective noun in:

a .... of cotton	a .... of singers
a .... of insects	a .... of angels
a .... of directors	a .... of ladies
a .... of rags	a .... of eggs.

6. Complete the similes:
He was as .... as a monkey.
It was as .... as a rock.
That story is as .... as the hills.
The old gentleman was as .... as Punch.
The patient was as .... as a sheet.

7. Add a suitable word:
Train is to station as steamer is to ....
Joy is to smile as .... is to tears.
Solid is to liquid as .... is to water.
Fish is to fin as bird is to ....
Circle is to semi-circle as two is to ....

8. Describe briefly:
(a) How you would clean a pair of shoes;
or
(b) How you would make a pot of tea for two.

EXERCISE 20

1. Write sentences using these:
Lean and lanky;   Old and grey;   Rack and ruin;
High and low;   Thick and thin.

2. Add a word to describe the sound made in the following:
I heard the .... of the drum in the distance.
They could hear the .... of leaves in the trees.
In the haunted house the .... of chains could be heard.
I was frightened by the .... of thunder.
The car stopped with a .... of brakes.

3. Write in full:
A.A.; B.Sc.; Co.; H.R.H.; C.I.D.; Y.M.C.A.; B.R.; C.O.D.; e.g.; i.e.

4. By means of a prefix, give the opposite to:

direct	....	happy	....	noble	....
wise	....	sense	....	regular	....
sane	....	legal	....	human	....
correct	....				

5. Form an adverb from:

critical ....   sweet ....   true ....

pure ....   heavy ....   simple ....

wide ....   happy ....

6. Explain the meaning of:

To hit the nail on the head.   To turn over a new leaf.

To rain cats and dogs.   To hang one's head.

7. Punctuate:

Wait shouted the policeman I would like a word with you

Lucy asked do you think my brother will come

Hullo I asked where do you think youre going

8. Write a short composition on:

(a) My favourite T.V. programme;

or

(b) My last visit to the dentist.

EXERCISE 21

1. Insert the correct punctuation and quotation marks in these sentences:

Please miss asked Lucy where shall I sit

The mistress replied you can sit here

Lucy said thank you and made her way to the seat

2. Replace the words in italics by one word, so that the meaning is the same:

The noise was no longer *able to be heard*.

In such heat, nothing could *keep alive*.

The song was signed by the *man who wrote it*.

He used to come here *from time to time*.

3. Fill in the missing word:

The notice said, "Fishing strictly ...."

The third .... was scored by the centre-forward.

I visited the doctor's .... yesterday.

I placed flowers on the graves in the ....

4. Use the correct relative pronoun from this list, to complete the sentences:
   Who, which, what, that.
   The boy .... is ill, is my best friend.
   May has a sister .... is learning to dance.
   The furniture .... arrived was very costly.
   I saw several carts .... were loaded with hay.
   I could not imagine .... had caused it.

5. Use another word instead of *funny* in:
   How funny to meet you here.
   We saw a funny sight at the fair.
   The animal made a funny noise.
   That book is really funny.
   It seemed a funny thing to do.

6. Make a list of the adjectives in the following passage:
   "Oh, but he was a tight-fisted hand at the grindstone. A squeezing, wrenching, grasping, scraping, clutching, covetous old sinner."
   A Christmas Carol, by Charles Dickens

7. Write sentences to show the difference between:
   Council, counsel;   licence, license;   advise, advice;
   profit, prophet;   whether, weather.

8. Write a composition on:
   (a) A camping holiday;
   or
   (b) Lost in the forest.

EXERCISE 22

1. Give one word for:
   A ship that travels under water ....
   A sailor's map ....
   An instrument that makes distant objects look nearer ....
   An instrument used for drawing circles ....

2. Explain the meaning of:
    To nip in the bud;   To lead a dog's life;
    To bury the hatchet;   To throw up the sponge;
    To burn the candle at both ends.

3. Punctuate, inserting quotation marks where necessary:
    What time are you leaving asked my uncle
    The boy asked his friend are you going home no replied the boy Im on my
    way to the cinema
    Dont I yelled youre hurting me

4. Complete these by using a suitable word:
    The tramp asked for a .... of bread.
    It was as tiny as a .... of sand.
    I added a .... of salt to the soup.
    There wasn't a .... of light to be seen.
    It added a .... of colour to the room.

5. Without using *and*, *but*, or *so*, join these sentences:
    (a) I was watching the game. I saw an aeroplane overhead.
    (b) The building was opened. It was built by my father.
    (c) The boy could not run. He had hurt his ankle.
    (d) I heard children singing. I was passing the school

6. Give a word similar in meaning to:
    deceive   ....   maximum   ....
    assemble   ....   suspended   ....
    feeble   ....   hoax   ....
    comprehend   ....   rough   ....

7. Write down the word which does not fit:
    Apple, banana, pear, plum, greengage.
    Iron, tin, glass, copper, lead.
    Table, chair, stool, sofa, bench.
    Tulip, narcissus, daffodil, primrose, snowdrop.

8. Write a story ending with:
    ". . . and I have made up my mind I will never go skating again; unless the ice
    is really safe."

1. Put in the capital letters and punctuation marks:
    the names of the brothers were john tom peter and harry
    oil is found in iran iraq and america
    i dont understand i murmured jane promised to call here on wednesday

2. Write in the plural:
    The lady nursed the baby.
    The knife was lying near the child.
    The man bought a calf.
    This is the place where I work.
    The girl's stocking was torn.

3. Change the masculine to feminine:
    The wizard frightened the fox.
    The monk spoke to the duke.
    The man-servant and his son-in-law quarrelled.
    The prince proved a good host.
    My grandfather owns a nice colt.

4. Complete these sentences:
    His face was as red as a ....
    This place seems safe as ....
    At full-back, he was as .... as a rock.
    She was as .... as a cucumber.
    The twins were as like as ....

5. Give one word for:
    A place where wild animals are kept.
    A place where gas is stored.
    A place where aeroplanes are kept under cover.
    A place where films are shown to the public.
    A place where grain is stored.

6. Write sentences containing the following:
    | Fair and square; | Heart and soul; | Hammer and tongs; |
    | Head and shoulders; | One and only. | |

7. Give a word opposite in meaning to:
    | permanent | .... | humble | .... |
    | rapid | .... | entrance | .... |
    | familiar | .... | quiet | .... |
    | purchase | .... | inferior | .... |

8. Write a reply to this advertisement:
    Wanted by Grocery Store, boy or girl, just left school. Apply in own handwriting to:

    Box 24, c/o *Daily Gazette*, Romford.

EXERCISE 24

1. Write in full:

bus	....	plane	....	gym	....
specs	....	pram	....	photo	....
exam	....	phone	....		

2. By means of a prefix, make a word opposite in meaning to:

audible	....	lock	....
visible	....	screw	....
connect	....	famous	....
perfect	....	legible	....

3. Select the correct word from each of the brackets, and write out the sentence:
    I cannot (bare, bear) much (pain, pane).
    He tried to (steal, steel) the (sent, scent).
    I (new, knew) his (aunt, ant) quite well.
    The (rays, raise) of the (son, sun) were warm.
    Mother (made, maid) some (plane, plain) cake.

4. Explain the meaning of:
    (a) Half a loaf is better than no bread.
    (b) It's a long lane that has no turning.
    (c) A small leak will sink a big ship.
    (d) Absence makes the heart grow fonder.

5. Correct:
    (a) He is not as old as me.
    (b) Me and my friend is going fishing.
    (c) Which is the tallest, Jim or Margaret?
    (d) Pass me them apples.

6. Copy these headings to give four columns:
    Masculine   Feminine   Common   Neuter
    Now place the following words in the correct column, according to the gender:
    Lion, cousin, princess, desk, parent, nephew, son, aunt, ewe, pencil, door.

7. Fill in the spaces with the sound made:

the dog ....   the donkey ....
the pig ....   the bull ....
the elephant ....   the ape ....

8. Write a letter to your father, who is away on business, telling him all the local news.

EXERCISE 25

1. Add a suitable subject to make a sentence:
.... scored a wonderful goal.   .... ran like a hare.
.... boiled over.   .... fell with a thud.
.... rustled in the breeze.

2. Complete:
Up is to down as .... is to low.
Swan is to .... as dog is to puppy.
Horse is to stable as hare is to ....
Foot is to .... as hand is to glove.
Mutton is to sheep as .... is to calf.

3. Write in full:—
Cres.; N.B.; h.p.; R.A.C.; N.Z.; R.I.P.; Dr.; No.

4. Give a word opposite in meaning to:
generous ....   motorist ....
senior ....   worse ....
deny ....   multiply ....
defend ....   mountain ....

5. Use the correct word from the brackets:
I bought a pound of (stake, steak) to (roost, roast).
The (cellar, seller) was (to, two, too) damp.
I asked (hymn, him) not to (meddle, medal) with it.
The (boy, buoy) wanted (hire, higher) wages.
Of (coarse, course) it was a big (gambol, gamble).

6. Form adjectives from:
anxiety ....   tide ....
picture ....   gold ....
sympathy ....   danger ....
affection ....   brass ....
bible ....   poison ....

7. Explain the meaning of:

        On the square;   An old salt;

        Hard up;   At a loose end;

        To make a clean breast of.

8. Write a composition of about 15 lines on:

    (a) Hiking;

    or

    (b) Our village/town.

EXERCISE 26

1. Give one word for:

        A small printed sheet of paper.

        An imaginary line round the middle of the earth.

        A soldier with three stripes on each arm.

        The person who controls a cricket match.

        The middle part of an apple.

2. Place the following words in two columns, present or past tense:

        Came, sing, ate, decided, went, ask, dream, used, sleep, reply, said, flow.

3 Form a noun from:

cruel	....	enjoy	....
cash	....	begin	....
young	....	remember	....
punish	....	injure	....

4. Give a word similar in meaning to:

lament	....	conceal	....
stern	....	omen	....
yearly	....	prompt	....
unite	....	odour	....

5. Write in full:

        I haven't told him that we'll be there.

        We've no reason to doubt that he's coming.

        I'm afraid there isn't any hope.

        You needn't worry as 'tis not your fault.

        You'll find that I've already sent the message.

6. Put a suitable word in the space to complete each sentence:

I heard the .... of the whip.

The .... of the bullet startled me.

From the smithy came the .... of an anvil.

The .... of the explosion was heard for miles.

The engine stopped with a .... of steam.

7. Use inverted commas to punctuate the following in two different ways, so that each has two different meanings:

John said Mary has just gone out.

Frank shouted Tom I want you.

8. Write a composition on:

(a) A famous person who lives to-day;

or

(b) A famous person, now dead.

EXERCISE 27

1. Each of the following words has two plural forms. Write six sentences containing these plurals:

Brother; penny; cloth.

2. Give one word for:

a young trout	....	a young bird	....
a young salmon	....	a young swan	....
a young eel	....		

3. Fill in the spaces with a collective noun:

I watched a .... of aeroplanes at the display.

The road was being repaired by a .... of labourers.

The town was protected by a .... of machine guns.

The duchess wore a .... of beautiful pearls.

A .... of policemen chased the escaped prisoner.

4. Substitute one word for those in italics:

My mother *came into* the room.

The game was *put off* until Thursday.

I will *go with* you to the concert.

My friend *went over* the road to the other side.

The new teacher would not *put up with* any nonsense.

5. Form an adjective from the following by means of the suffix "able" or "ible":

invis	....	reason	....
accept	....	consider	....
aud	....	respons	....
suscept	....	fees	....
sens	....		

6. Form a noun from:

lose	....	judge	....	mock	....
free	....	real	....	provide	....
simple	....	explain	....	just	....

7. Explain the meaning of:
   To hold one's tongue. To kick up a dust.
   To let the cat out of the bag. To send packing.

8. Write an account of any dream you have had.

EXERCISE 28

1. Rearrange these subjects and predicates to form sensible sentences:

The new ships	like woodwork.
The burglar	is afraid of mice.
The wrist watch	was blind.
My dog	cut the telephone wires.
Most boys	won't bite.
The poor old man	was stolen.
The little girl	belonged to the navy.

2. Substitute one word for those in italics:
   The *designer of the building* is dead.
   The new town has a large *number of inhabitants*.
   The cook used the *yellow part* of the egg.
   The actor gave me his *signature in his own writing*.

3. Write a word similar in meaning to:

broad	....	mad	....
nimble	....	wealth	....
option	....	prohibit	....
halt	....	exterior	....

4. Use in sentences:
    Over and over;   Hale and hearty;
    Rant and rave;   Come and go;
    Ups and downs.

5. Punctuate, putting in quotation marks, etc.:
    Where were you this morning asked the teacher please sir replied peter I had
    to run messages for my father.

6. Form a verb from:
    able   ....   custom   ....
    peril   ....   soft   ....
    terror   ....   joy   ....
    education   ....   deed   ....

7. The following words have two different meanings. Write sentences, using the
    words so that the different meanings are shown:
    Conduct, train, bear, felt, peer.

8. Describe what you would do if:
    (a) You noticed a strong smell of gas in the room.
    (b) A fire was smoking heavily.

EXERCISE 29

1. Form compound nouns by joining the following words in pairs:
    Dust, master, pick, mill, house, head, black, piece, pan, office, coal, board,
    pond, ache, axe, post.

2. Complete the following by inserting the collective noun:
    I had a .... of tools for my birthday.
    There was a .... of monkeys at the circus.
    A .... of wool arrived at the factory.
    The grocer unpacked a .... of fruit.
    We passed a .... of islands on the trip.

3. Arrange the following genders in four columns:—
    Masculine   Feminine   Common   Neuter
    Woman, gate, duke, pupil, friend, niece, truck, uncle, poet, goddess, animal,
    hill.

4. Complete these similes:
   He was reputed to be as .... as Solomon.
   The old man was as .... as a post.
   I felt as .... as a daisy after the game.
   My new coat kept me as .... as a bone.
   The prisoner said with a smile, "I was as .... as a judge."

5. Name the kind of shop where you would expect to find:
   Tea, sugar, rice, cheese.
   Bananas, apples, pears, peaches.
   Cough mixture, aspirins, toothpaste, bandages.
   Saucepans, nails, saws, hammers.
   Sheets, tablecloths, curtain material, tape.

6. Use the correct word from each of the brackets:
   He cut the (vain, vein) in his wrist with a razor blade.
   The house was built on a new (sight, site).
   I bought a new fishing (real, reel).
   The (whole, hole) of the programme was poor.
   She was the (bell, belle) of the ball.

7. Form an adjective from:

accident	....	athlete	....
pride	....	truth	....
Italy	....	life	....
duty	....	iron	....

8. Write a description of:
   (a) A week on a farm
   or
   (b) A week at the seaside.

EXERCISE 30

1. Rearrange these subjects and predicates to form proper sentences:—

My father	likes playing marbles.
The elephant	has a faulty valve.
The nut	jumped from the engine.
The little boy	is manager of the bank.
My radio	had a bitter taste.
The new driver	is very strong.

2. Form a verb from:

actor .... bath ....
rich .... thought ....
short .... growth ....
false .... grief ....
glory .... force ....

3. Write the past tense of:

arise .... bite ....
feel .... keep ....
stroke .... freeze ....
spring .... begin ....

4. Compare these adjectives:

gracious .... much ....
ill .... famous ....
glorious .... big ....
tight .... useful ....

5. Complete these proverbs:

Charity .... First come ....
No news is .... Union ....

6. Give one word for:

A doctor who performs operations. ....
A lady who makes and sells hats. ....
A place where photographs are taken. ....
The air surrounding the earth. ....
A place where you can buy meals. ....

7. Punctuate the following sentence by inserting the inverted commas, so that it has two different meanings:

Jack said mother will be home later

8. Describe any article you have made, and describe how you made it.

EXERCISE 31

1. Use a pronoun instead of the word in italics:

David and *David's* dog are great friends.
As soon as the girls arrived, *the girls* started singing.
If I find Henry, *Henry and I* will play games.
I asked Molly if *Molly* liked Blackpool.
Susie and *Susie's* friend called yesterday.

2. Make a list of the verbs in this paragraph:

He arrived at school and entered the classroom. He placed his books in his locker and then returned to the playground to meet his friends. When the bell rang, all the pupils ran to their lines and marched into the main hall.

3. Add a suitable adverb to the following:

He is sleeping ....
He talks about his work ....
She sings ....
The cock crows .... in the morning.
I am going ....
He did it ....
They all laughed ....

4. Select the correct word from the brackets:

What (is, his) the cause of (is, his) illness?
(Where, Were) you at the market in (their, there) car?
She is (has, as) happy (as, has) a lark.
(His, Is) this (is, his) hat?

5. Explain the meaning of:

A red letter day;   As the crow flies;
A fly in the ointment;   A blind alley;
A flash in the pan.

6. Correct these sentences:

They have did it again.
This book is different to mine.
He hurted his ankle in the football match.
Where is my shoes?
Me and Sam went fishing.

7. The following words can have two different meanings. Write sentences to show this difference:

Notice, fair, lock, common, grate.

8. Write a story entitled:

My life story by
(a) A dirty £1 note;
or
(b) A well-worn garden spade.

1. Write the following in the plural:
    The fairy's dance;   That man;
    This lady;   My baby's cot;
    It was the woman's shoe.

2. Write out the following and underline the adjectives:
    Under the spreading chestnut tree
    The village smithy stands.
    The smith a mighty man is he,
    With large and sinewy hands.

3. Write out these sentences, using the past tense of the verb in brackets:
    Mother .... me a pair of shoes.   (buy)
    The baby .... over the floor.   (creep)
    The old lady .... at the altar.   (kneel)
    The wounded soldier .... the pain.   (bear)
    He .... when the dog bit him.   (cry)

4. Punctuate:
    Stay where you are he cried or I will shoot
    We werent sure of the place answered the boy
    I asked the policeman which bus will take me to the Zoo
    Open the window said mother its very close

5. Make sentences to show what each of the following does:
    a journalist   ....   a florist   ....
    a dentist   ....   a conductor   ....
    a dispenser   ....   an optician   ....

6. Put in the correct preposition:
    The apple was shared (between, among) the two boys.
    Your hat fell (in, into) the pond.
    Her work is different (from, to) mine.
    I shared the sweets (between, among) the five children.

7. Complete by using an adjective formed from the word in brackets:
    He let out a .... yell.   (fiend)
    The clown did some .... tricks.   (acrobat)
    Deserting is a .... action.   (coward)
    Bombs are very .... weapons.   (destroy)
    He was a .... type of person   (misery)

8. Write a story of an adventure you have had, ending your story with the words:
". . . and I certainly do not want to go there again."

EXERCISE 33

1. Complete the sentences by using the most suitable of these conjunctions:
   Although, but, because, and, unless, since.
   We hit the stone hard, ... could not break it.
   I missed the trip .... I had a cold.
   I have not seen my brother .... he emigrated.
   I will try to play, ... I do not feel well.
   The teacher told him he would be punished .... his work improved.
   I slipped on the pavement .... fell.

2. Give the plural of:
   cupful   ....   by-way   ....
   man-of war   ....   passer-by   ....
   maid-of honour ....   Commander-in-chief   ....

3. Fill in the following four columns with the words:
   Witch, ram, child, filly, floor, driver, landlord, owner, kitten, pencil, sister, hero.

   Masculine   *Feminine*   *Common*   *Neuter*

4. Complete the similes:
   She was as .... as a lamb.
   That man is as .... as a gorilla.
   The new player is as .... as mustard.
   The place was as .... as the grave.
   It tasted as .... as honey.

5. The following sentences are in indirect speech. Put them into direct speech, by using inverted commas:
   The waiter told the customers that roast lamb was not available.
   The magistrate told the witness that he did not think he was telling the truth.
   The clergyman asked my sister if she would like to take part in the play.

6. Give one word for:
   A man who always looks on the bright side.
   Children forming a class in school.
   A person who lives alone.
   A man who tracks down criminals.
   A man who attends to fires on board ship.

7. Explain the meaning of:
   Horse play;   A cat on hot bricks;
   A dead cert;   To chew the fat;
   Not a patch on.

8. Describe an ordinary day in the life of:
   (a) A policeman on point duty;   or   *(b)* A hospital nurse.

EXERCISE 34

1. Add "ing" to the following words, making any necessary alterations in spelling:
   cycle   ....   life   ....   swim   ....
   occur   ....   begin   ....   move   ....
   sit   ....

2. Write sentences using each of the following words:
   To, too, two; Air, hair, heir; Rain, reign, rein.

3. The following words can have two different meanings. Write sentences to show this difference:
   Bay, port, vice, pound, pine.

4. Substitute one word for those in italics:
   The lane seemed *to have no end.*
   The man agreed to *make an apology.*
   He approached the bend *with caution.*
   The mechanic did the work *with great skill.*
   His work was *without a blemish.*

5. Give the opposite to:
   liquid   ....   profit   ....   reward   ....
   giant   ....   famine   ....   guilt   ....
   hatred   ....   noble   ....

6. Write the past tense of:
   go   ....   seek   ....   take   ....
   lie   ....   drive   ....   lose   ....
   burn   ....   round   ....

7. Correct the following sentences:
   Please except my apology
   If we don't hurry, we will loose the train.
   I seen him on the way home.
   The woman had fell over the cliff.
   The audience begun to applaud.

8. Explain what you would do if:
   (a) Curtains in your room caught fire.
   (b) A water pipe burst due to the frost.

EXERCISE 35

1. Write in the plural form:
   This book is mine.
   I gave a lift to my friend.
   That orange is rotten.
   He asked me to accompany him.
   I hope you will come to my party.

2. What did the boy mean when he wrote:
   Herrings swim in shawls.
   The lambs were gambling in the field.
   The Gulf Stream is a warm currant.
   Cereals are films shown in parts.
   A sextant is a man who digs graves.

3. Write the following to give the opposite:
   The tide was ebbing fast.
   The ascent was made with difficulty.
   The river was falling slowly.
   The positive terminal of the battery was damaged.

4. Explain the meaning of the words in italics:
   This is the *thin edge of the wedge.*
   His success in the examination *turned his head.*
   You should *put your shoulder to the wheel.*
   He acts like a *dog in the manger.*

5. Form an abstract noun from:

ignorant	....	modest	....
move	....	hard	....
honest	....	true	....
joyful	....	sad	....
elevate	....	free	....

6. The following words can have two different meanings. Write sentences to show the difference:
   Dock, lay, sound, stroke, drill.

7. Use the correct word from the brackets:
   Over a (weak, week) has (past, passed) since I met him.
   This is a new (style, stile) in men's (suites, suits).
   It is (rude, rood) to (stair, stare) at people.
   I (herd, heard) him shout (aloud, allowed).

8. Write a letter to a farmer who is advertising for a boy who is keen to learn farming;
   or
   To a dressmaker who needs a young person to learn the trade.

EXERCISE 36

1. Give the opposite of:

enemy	....	feeble	....
fertile	....	polite	....
arrive	....	coarse	....
contract	....	refuse	....
disperse	....		

2. Put suitable words in the spaces to show the sounds made:

The .... of an engine.	The .... of a horn.
The .... of bells.	The .... of coins.
The .... of chains.	The .... of paper.
The .... of a bow.	The .... of corks.

3. Give one word for:
   A place where orphans live.
   A place where operations are performed in hospital.
   A place where criminals are sent.
   A place where clothes are sent to be washed.

4. Rearrange these correctly:

Birds bleat; a cat grunts; a dog neighs; donkeys sing; a frog hoots; a pig purrs; a serpent croaks; an owl barks; a horse brays; a lamb hisses.

5. Put into direct speech:

The man told me that he would not be able to keep the appointment.
The traveller asked me where I lived.

6. Complete the proverbs:

One good turn	....	Make hay	....
One man's meat	....	Look before	....
Penny wise	....		

7. Use the correct word from the brackets:

We found some (muscles, mussels) on the (beech, beach).
I called at the (counsel, council) office to (licence, license) the car.
The climate (effected, affected) the popularity of the (place, plaice).
He (through, threw) a bun to the (bear, bare).

8. Condense the following to a telegram of 12 words, including the address and sender's name:

Mr. John Wilson, "Avoca," High Street, Reading.
Goods were despatched on train which arrives at Reading at 3 o'clock to-day.
Please meet this train.   Mills Radio Ltd.

EXERCISE 37

1. Fill in a suitable preposition:—

You must abide .... the rules of the club.
I congratulate you .... your promotion.
She used to correspond .... him regularly.
The solicitor decided to look .... the case.
She could not point a finger .... him.

2. Explain the meaning of:

Off colour;	the off chance;	a goody-goody;
a good for nothing;	riding a high horse;	flogging a dead horse.

3. Write these in a shortened form:
   A hat belonging to Tom.
   The room belonging to the dentist.
   The bicycle belonging to my son.
   The desks belonging to the pupils.
   The hoofs of the horses.

4. What person would you associate with:

an awl	....	a baton	....
a hod	....	a palette	....
a plane	....	a sextant	....
a stethoscope	....	a spanner	....

5. Write one word for:
   The ministers forming the government.
   Many ships ready to defend the country.
   Father, mother and their children.
   A number of people singing together.

6. Add "ence", "ance" or "ense" to the following:—

penit	....	imm	....	emin	....
inc	....	dist	....	brilli	....

7. Two of the following proverbs seem to have opposite meanings. Write out the two:
   Too many cooks spoil the broth.
   It is never too late to mend.
   Many hands make light work.
   A rolling stone gathers no moss.

8. Describe one of the following:
   (a) A caravan holiday;
   or
   (b) What I would do to improve the district in which I live.

EXERCISE 38

1. Rewrite the following without using "lot" or "lots":
   I have been to Cardiff lots of times.
   There were a lot of flies near the jam.
   Lots of people like cycling.
   There was a lot of cement in the stores.

2. Complete the following (the first is done for you):

   I choose   I chose   I have chosen

   I swim ....

   I write ....

   I ring ....

   I throw ....

   I ride ....

   I drink ....

3. Rearrange the subjects and predicates to make sensible sentences:

   A gold watch   joined the army.

   His brother   can carry many passengers.

   Every dog   can bathe in a saucer.

   An air liner   was stolen from his house.

   The goldfinch   should have a stamp on it.

   Every letter   should wear a collar.

4. Rewrite, substituting one word for those in italics:

   She is a person who is *liked by everyone*.

   I *made up my mind* to resign.

   The judge decided that the prisoner was *free from guilt*.

   He overcame the difficulty *step by step*.

   The man wanted to *leave home and go* to Canada.

5. Use the correct word in the brackets:

   I (rode, rowed) the boat over to the (reads, reeds).

   The cat held a (piece, peace) of meat in her (pause, paws).

   The carpenter has (bean, been) sharpening his (plane, plain).

   I bought a (frieze, freeze) for (hour, our) front room.

6 Correct these sentences:

   That is the horse what won the race.

   Where is the person which did this?

   The man from who I bought the dog lives near me.

   He took by far the biggest half of the apple,

   Fred and Wilfred play well, but Fred is the best.

7. Explain the meaning of:

   The black sheep of the family;   A square peg in a round hole;

   To play second fiddle;   To hit the headlines.

8. Write a letter to your cousin, explaining why you cannot come to his/her birthday party.

EXERCISE 39

1. Complete the similes:

As easy as	....	As sound as	....
As large as	....	As stiff as	....
As pale as	....	As playful as	....
As true as	....	As thin as	....

2. Form a noun from the word in capitals and use it in the sentence:

FAMOUS   The footballer's .... soon spread.
HIGH   The aeroplane flew at a great ....
CURIOUS   My .... nearly got me into trouble.
BEAUTIFUL   She was surprised at the .... of the scenery.
PROVE   He was asked for .... of his charge.

3. Form an adjective from:

victory	....	skill	....
meddle	....	science	....
mercy	....	fool	....
coward	....	caution	....

4. Correct the following:

Can I go to the cinema tonight?
The man is going to learn me to play the piano.
She could not come quicker.
The boy admitted he done it himself.
I have forgot to deliver the message.
The little girl sings quite nice.

5. Explain the meaning of:

Carried away;   Under a cloud;   At loggerheads;
Stuck up;   To show a clean pair of heels.

6. Give one word for:

A man who tends fires on a railway engine.
A sailor's map.
A place from which stone and slate is obtained.
Low ground between two hills.
A person who makes up medicine for a doctor.

7. Complete the following:

A nun lives in a ....   A hare lives in a ....
A prisoner sleeps in a ....   A dog lives in a ....
A Swiss peasant lives in a ....

8. The following is part of a story:

    "Slowly, hardly daring to make a sound, we approached the empty house. Our hearts were pounding madly. Suddenly . . ."

    Write a story, telling what happened before and after the above situation.

EXERCISE 40

1. Write out the following sentences, using the correct word from the brackets:

    They had just (went, gone) to the pictures.

    The telephone (rang, rung) loudly.

    He was (given, gave) a letter to post.

    They soon (begun, began) to search for the money.

    We (past, passed) the policeman near the corner.

2. Form a noun from each of these words:

    reveal   ....   live   ....
    revive   ....   civilise ....
    depart   ....   imitate   ....
    move   ....   music   ....

3. Give one word for:

    A man who studies the stars.   A man about to be married.
    A place where beer is made.   A story with a moral.
    A man who measures land.

4. Write out the following sentences, using the correct word from each bracket:

    I (guest, guessed) the price of the (pail, pale).

    The (colonel, kernel) was very (poplar, popular).

    He paid by (cheque, check) for the (fir, fur) coat.

    The village (quire, choir) sang at the (fete, fate).

5. In the following sentences, use a word from:

    Cried, shouted, snapped, whispered, replied, asked,

    instead of the word *said*:

    "I don't know what to do," said Mary.

    "Wait!" he said, "I'd like a word with you."

    "Where shall I meet you?" he said.

    "No!" she said, her eyes flashing, "I will not agree."

    "Be careful," she said, "he may hear us."

    "Come over to this side," said my friend, who had crossed the river.

6. Change into direct speech:
   I inquired if the new garage had opened last week.
   John asked Robert if he was going to the circus.
   The patient asked the nurse if he might read a book.

7. Rewrite the following, using a word opposite in meaning to those in italics:
   A *careful* motorist is *wise*.
   She *lowered* the lamp *slowly*.
   The *man* was *rich*.
   He had *many* supporters.

8. Make up a short story to illustrate one of the following proverbs:
   (a) Easy come, easy go.
   (b) New brooms sweep clean

Printed by Bell & Bain, Ltd., Glasgow.